children's sunnyday songbook

Arranged by Bert Brewis

CONTENTS

Edited by PETER FOSS
First Published 1987
© International Music Publications Limited
Southend Road, Woodford Green,
Essex IG8 8HN, England.

215-2-420

Bring Me Sunshine

Words by SYLVIA DEE
Music by ARTHUR KENT

Congratulations

Words and Music by
BILL MARTIN and PHIL COULTER

5

Everything Is Beautiful

Words and Music
by RAY STEVENS

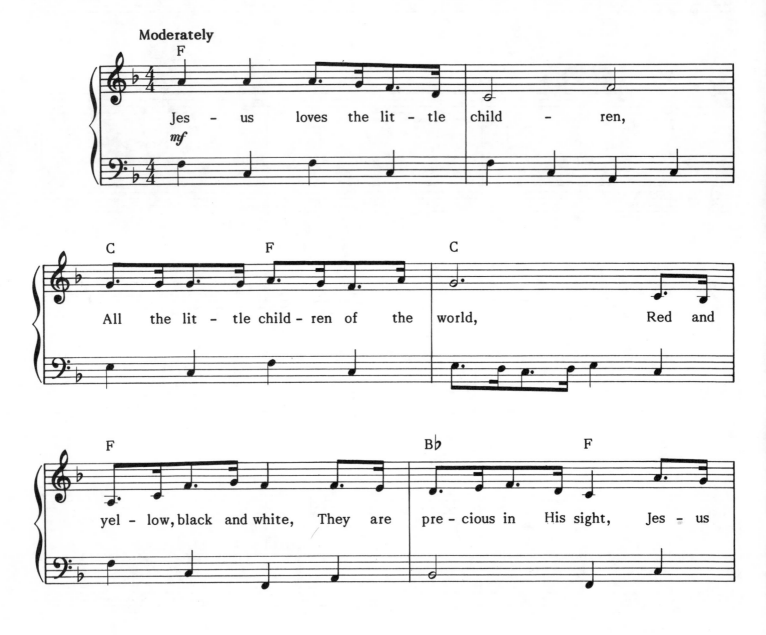

10

Dancing In The Street

Words and Music by WILLIAM STEVENSON,
MARVIN GAYE and IVY HUNTER

The Floral Dance

Words and Music
by KATIE MOSS

Ev-'ry boy took a girl round the waist, And hur-ried her off in tremend-ous haste,

poco accel.

Whether they knew one anoth-er I care not, Whether they-cared at all, I know not; But they

poco rit.

kissed—— as they danced—— a - long.

a tempo

And

there was that band with that curious tone, Of the cor-net, clar-i-net and big trom-bone.

Fid-dle, 'cel-lo, big bass drum; Bas - soon, flute and eu-phon - i - um,

Happy Days Are Here Again

Words by JACK YELLEN
Music by MILTON AGER

Matchstalk Men
And Matchstalk Cats And Dogs

Words and Music by
MICHAEL COLEMAN and BRIAN BURKE

28

29

The Lambeth Walk

Words by DOUGLAS FURBER
Music by NOEL GAY

Living Doll

Words and Music
by LIONEL BART

On The Sunny Side Of The Street

Words by DOROTHY FIELDS
Music by JIMMY McHUGH

38

Postman Pat

Words and Music
by BRYAN DALY

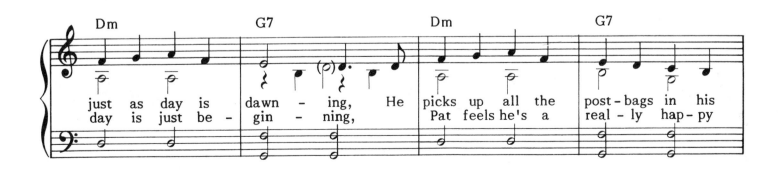

40

Spread A Little Happiness

Words by CLIFFORD GREY
Music by VIVIAN ELLIS

The Smurf Song

Words by PIERRE KARTNER
English Lyrics by LINDA LEE
Music by PIERRE KARTNER

2. Can you crawl thru' a water tap?
Yes we smurf thru' a water tap.
And climb thru' a small key-hole?
Yes, and through a small key-hole.
Can you play a tune on a flute?
Smurfing the flute we think so cute.
Do smurfs like to dance and croon?
Yes, but only to this tune.

3. Tell me why are smurfs so small?
We're not small, but you are tall.
Do you wear your caps in bed?
Yes, our caps stay on our head.
Do you go to sleep till dawn?
Yes, but first two times we yawn.
Tell me what is your request?
Smurfing, that's what we like best.

Summer Holiday

Words and Music by
BRUCE WELCH and BRIAN BENNETT

Tomorrow

Words by MARTIN CHARNIN
Music by CHARLES STROUSE

The Sun Has Got His Hat On

Words and Music by
RALPH BUTLER and NOEL GAY

Tie A Yellow Ribbon
'round The Ole Oak Tree

Words and Music by
IRWIN LEVINE and L RUSSELL BROWN

Walking In The Air

Words and Music
by HOWARD BLAKE

Sud-den-ly   swooping low   on an o – cean deep,

rous-ing up   a   might-y mon — ster   from   his

You're A Pink Toothbrush

Words and Music by RALPH RUVIN, BOB HALFIN,
HAROLD IRVING and JOHNNY SHERIDAN

When You're Smiling

Words and Music by MARK FISHER,
JOE GOODWIN and LARRY SHAY

69

You Are My Sunshine

Words and Music by
JIMMIE DAVIS and CHARLES MITCHELL

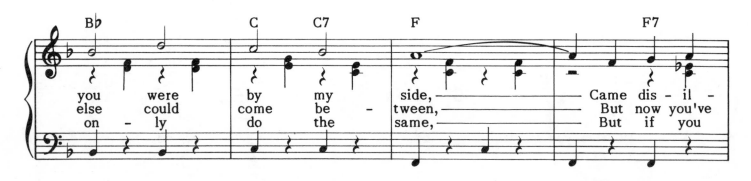

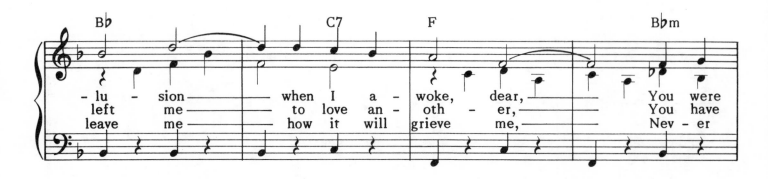

Y Viva Espana

Original Words by LEO ROZENSTRAETEN
English Lyrics by EDDIE SEAGO
Music by LEO CAERTS

73

2. Quite by chance to hot romance I found the answer
Flamenco dancers are far the finest bet
There was one who whispered "Whoo hasta la vista"
Each time I kissed him behind the castanet
He rattled his maracas close to me
In no time I was trembling at the knee.

(Chorus)

3. When they first arrive the girls are pink and pasty
But oh so tasty as soon as they go brown
I guess they know every fellow will be queueing
To do the wooing his girlfriend won't allow,
But still I think today's a lucky day
That's why I've learned to shout "ole."

(Chorus)

You're Never Fully Dressed Without A Smile

Words by MARTIN CHARNIN
Music by CHARLES STROUSE

78